The ABCs
of Learning About Careers

by Dwayne Douglas
Illustrated by Arsal

ISBN: 978-1-7333140-2-2 (hardback)
978-1-7333140-4-6 (paperback)

Any references to historical events, real people, or real places are used fictitiously.
Characters and places are products of the illustrator's imagination.

Illustrated by Arsal
Edited by Rochelle Douglas

Writer.TDDouglas Publishing

Writer.TDDouglas
PO Box 72
Smyrna, TN 37167-9998

Since this book is about careers, when I think
about my career, I'd like to give special thanks to…

Billy Summers

Brenda Triplett

Dr. Connie Jones

Dr. Gloria Bonner

Rochelle Douglas

Shawn Whitsell

Tamara Douglas

Will Shelton

I would like to also thank the principals (and assistant principals)
I have worked for over the years.

THANK YOU

With your career you can do anything or go to any place.

You can even be an Astronaut and travel outer space.

Do you believe that you can do anything?
If not, then you should.

Prepare now, and like a Barber or Beautician,
make sure your future looks good.

Creating new styles with clippers or curlers
sounds fun, many wish they could.

But maybe you can be a Carpenter
and make something from wood.

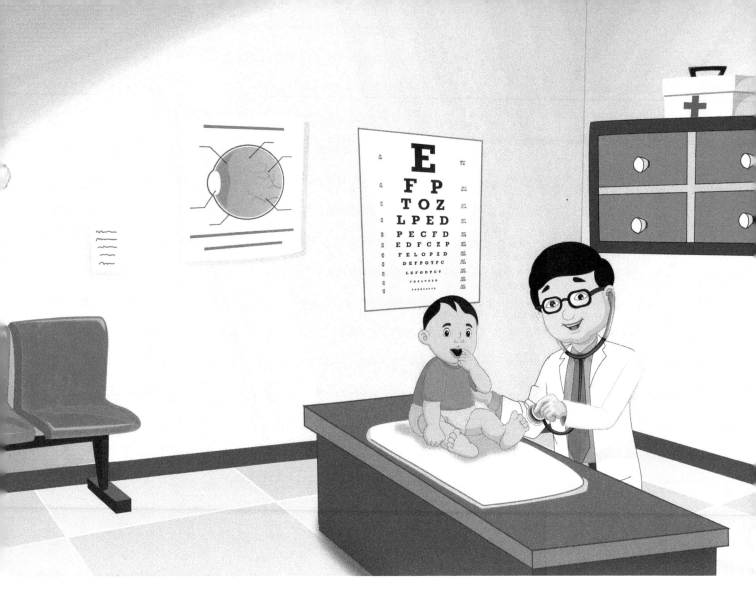

If people like what you make,
your products will probably sell.

If not, you can fix it like a Doctor,
and help the body get well.

Some careers are easy to get into, others
have challenges that are greater.

For example, it takes a lot of learning if you
want to be a public-school Educator.

College is not required for all careers,
but it could help your future to be brighter.

Another great career would be to
take on the life of a brave Firefighter.

Some careers will allow you to avoid a university and
stop you from listening to a professor or teacher.

But you must listen and learn from your trainer,
as if that person was a great Gospel Preacher.

Maybe you are a person full of talents and you can do it all.

Consider being a Handyman, there is a good
chance that somebody will call.

You can also use those hands to create software programs
or to fix a PC (Personal Computer).

If that sounds interesting, try a career
in IT (Information Technology).

Choosing your career can be a fun journey,
so hop on and enjoy the ride.

You can get advice from others, but like
a Judge, make sure you decide.

If you do what others want you to do, you may decide it was a mistake,
but at least the decision does not have to stick.

Making a bad decision can hurt like a Karate Instructor
using you to demonstrate a kick.

It's never too late to make a career change,
so you should smile and not frown.

Smile like a Lifeguard protecting children
so that nobody will drown.

While some careers keep you at a desk,
others let you move from place to place.

Sound interesting? You should be a
Mail Carrier if that's the case.

If you are curious about living things,
you should be a biologist.

But if you are curious about the mind,
you should consider being a Neurologist.

These careers can belong to you,
if you will have them to be.

If you can't visualize this, contact an
Optometrist to help you see.

With a good vision and some goals,
you will do as you please and will not fail.

You will have something positive to strive for and
the Police Officer won't have to take you to jail.

If you want to avoid jail, get rid of your
bad ways and eliminate wrath.

Just like a Quality Analyst,
I recommend changes in your path.

Remember that every Rapper won't get a deal.
Why? Because they all can't rap.

If an opportunity presents itself, don't jump
too fast and get caught in a trap.

Several musicians get stuck in deals and
must fight their way out in courts.

Speaking of fighting, another career many
people enjoy is one that involves Sports.

Being an athlete is hard because there is usually
somebody who is better, stronger, or faster.

But if you are not the one that's playing,
you can be a Television Broadcaster.

But your smile must be real;
you can't get on TV and be a faker.

Or the audience will harm your dreams and
the dreams may need an **U**ndertaker.

Learn to balance your life and
career like a person doing ballet.

Don't be on the move so much,
like a person working Valet.

Some people tip when they drop off cars;
some come back and tip later.

Tips are given in a lot of careers;
just ask a Waitress or Waiter.

Like an X-ray Technician, a good
boss can see through you.

Why waste your time on something
you don't want to do?

It's your future, don't let a
wonderful opportunity pass.

Get your mind and body right,
like a Yoga Instructor leading a class.

Letters A through Y named many careers;
hopefully you will consider a few.

If not, there are others, like a Zookeeper
taking care of animals in a zoo.

There are several needs that people
have on a day-to-day basis.

What is your gift that would put
a smile on some of their faces?

Printed in the USA
CPSIA information can be obtained
at www.ICGtesting.com
LVHW071521061023
760261LV00014B/659